SCHOLASTIC
Phonics

The Missing Treasure

Published in the UK by Scholastic Education, 2022

Scholastic Distribution Centre, Bosworth Avenue, Tournament Fields, Warwick, CV34 6UQ

Scholastic Ireland, 89E Lagan Road, Dublin Industrial Estate, Glasnevin, Dublin, D11 HP5F

SCHOLASTIC and associated logos are trademarks and/or registered trademarks of Scholastic Inc.
www.scholastic.co.uk
© 2022 Scholastic
1 2 3 4 5 6 7 8 9 2 3 4 5 6 7 8 9 0 1

Printed by Ashford Colour Press
The book is made of materials from well-managed, FSC®-certified forests
and other controlled sources.

A CIP catalogue record for this book is available from the British Library.

ISBN 978-0702-30928-1

Every effort has been made to trace copyright holders for the works reproduced in this publication,
and the publishers apologise for any inadvertent omissions.

Author
Suzy Ditchburn

Editorial team
Rachel Morgan, Vicki Yates, Tracy Kewley, Jennie Clifford

Design team
Dipa Mistry, Justin Hoffmann, Andrea Lewis, We Are Grace

Illustrations
Liliana Perez/Advocate Art

Can you spot the
hedgehog on 10 pages?

SCHOLASTIC

Help your child to read!

This book practises these letters and letter sounds.
Point and say the sounds with your child:

- ey (as in 'grey')
- kn (as in 'knee')
- eer (as in 'peered')
- su (as in 'treasure')
- dge (as in 'edge')
- y (as in 'pyramids')
- ti (as in 'information')
- ci (as in 'special')

Your child may need help to read these common tricky words:

- one
- were
- the
- any
- said
- two
- their
- beautiful
- thought
- to
- of
- who
- do
- are
- Mr
- our
- everyone

Before reading
- Look at the cover picture and read the title together. Read the back cover blurb to your child.
- Ask your child: *Have you ever found any treasure? Or have you ever found something buried that made you think it was treasure?*

During reading
- If your child gets stuck on a word, remind them to sound it out and then blend the sounds to read the word: kn-o-ck, knock.
- If they are still stuck, show them how to read the word.
- Enjoy looking at the pictures together. Pause to talk about the story.

After reading
- Ask your child: *Did the children do the right thing in taking the treasure home? Why?*
- *What would you do if you found some buried treasure?*

Lily and Toby lived near a large park.
One day, they were playing in the park when
Toby fell and caught his knee on something sharp.
They peered at the ground and spotted a shiny
object poking out.

They pulled it out.
It was a bowl with a sharp edge.
It had a fancy design on it.

"Is it real gold?" asked Lily.
"I don't know. Let's see if there's any more," said Toby.
They knelt down and dug.

Toby found two matching bowls.
Their fingers were cold and numb from digging.
Toby's knee was sore. But they kept going.
Lily found some beautiful jewels.

Where had the treasure come from? How did it get here?

Lily thought back to something they had been taught in school. They had learned about treasure like this. It was hidden in the pyramids in Egypt.

Suddenly, Lily heard a rustle in the leaves. "Let's go straight home," she said to Toby.

They rushed home and looked up information about Egyptian treasure on the internet.
There was an article about some missing treasure.
It had been stolen from the National Museum.

Knots of excitement filled their stomachs. But before they got carried away, they needed to talk to their dad.
He worked at the museum, so he knew all about Egyptian treasure.

The children had sent photos of the treasure to their dad. There was a knock at the door. Lily nudged Toby to cover up the treasure.

Outside was a tall lady with grey hair.
"I am from the museum," she explained to their mum, "I hear that you have discovered some Egyptian treasure."

Lily and Toby were confused.
"I wonder how she knows about it already,"
thought Toby.
"Maybe she saw us in the park," thought Lily.

Just then, Dad came home from work. He was wearing his museum uniform.
The lady peered at Dad's badge, edged away from the door and ran off up the street.

"How strange!" said Dad, "I wonder who she was. Now, show me the treasure! I want to know everything."

"This is the treasure that was stolen from the National Museum," said Dad. "It is ancient and very special. It comes from the pyramids of Egypt!"

"Do you think it was that lady who stole the treasure?" asked Lily.

"How did she get it? Did she break in?" said Toby.

"It's a mystery!" said Dad. "But we must get this
precious treasure straight back to the museum!"

"Your children are great treasure hunters," said Mr Lamb, the head of the museum.
"I know!" said Dad proudly.

"Thanks to your description, the thief has been caught," he told Lily and Toby.

"That's great news!" they cheered. "Our mission is complete!"

The next day, the children went back to the museum to see the treasure on display. It was all clean and shiny.

They got a special prize from Mr Lamb
for their good work.
"Three cheers for our treasure hunters!"
everyone shouted.

Retell the story